Stevie stared at the enormous trophy collection that was in the basement of his home. Those awards and trophies belonged to his father for many years of activities in various sports.

His father was a large man, tall and muscular. Stevie was small for his age, but hoped that one day he will be like his father.

Stevie enjoyed sports of every type. He and his father would sit for hours watching every channel that had sports activities. They would yell and holler at the television as if the referee could hear them.

He learned a lot from his father about sports. They talked about the hard work it takes to be the very best. He suggested Stevie find one sport that he liked and work hard to be the very best that he could be. "No matter what you choose, be proud of who you are, son."

Lying in bed that night, Stevie decided he would like to try out for a sport, but which one would it be?

Would he like to play soccer, basketball, baseball, swimming, or football? His father played in all of these sports.

The local Park District was having try-outs for various sports teams. Each day you could try-out for a different sport. This was exactly what Stevie wanted to do. Would he be able to play in all of the sports like his father?

Stevie arrived on Monday to try-out for the football squad. His father filled out the forms along with the other parents.

A loud whistle was blown and the boys were asked to line up by height. Stevie couldn't believe how small he looked compared to the other boys. He was the smallest boy in the group.

The coaches brought out huge boxes to the middle of the floor. Inside were uniforms and helmets for the boys to wear.

As the boys grabbed the uniforms and began putting them on, Stevie was not able to find one that he could fit. Everything was too large, even the helmet.

The coaches apologized, but Stevie was quite small for his age and there weren't any other uniforms available.
"We're proud of you for trying out anyway, son," said the coach.

Stevie was so disappointed that he asked his father to take him home. "Son, don't give up. You must always be proud of who you are. Maybe you could try-out for the baseball team tomorrow."

Baseball try-outs were crowded with plenty of boys wanting to make the team. Stevie was hoping this would be the sport for him to shine.
"I hope I'm not the shortest person to try-out for the squad," said Stevie.

The boys lined up in the gym as the coaches began choosing boys for their baseball team. All of the larger sized boys were chosen first. Stevie was still one of the smallest boys in the group.

He was disappointed that no one called his name for the first teams. He stood waiting for someone to choose him for the second squad team. He felt terrible standing there all alone.

His dad saw the look on Stevie's face. He walked up and took his hand. He was also disappointed that none of the coaches chose his son to be on the first team or second team.

"Let's go son," said his dad. "Maybe baseball is not the sport for you either. I'm still very, very proud of you for trying and not giving up. You'll find the sport that is just right for you."

During the week, Stevie tried out for the soccer and basketball squads. He discovered that these sports were also not for him. "Would I ever find the right sport for me?" thought Stevie.

At home, Stevie lay on his bed thinking about what he could do to make his dad really proud of him. He couldn't do any of the sports that his father could do. He was just too small.

Stevie clicked on the television to his favorite show. During a commercial, there was an advertisement for young people to try out at the local martial arts club.

"Wow!" said Stevie. "I never thought of martial arts!"

He explained to his father about the commercial.

"Are you sure you want to try out for another sport?" he asked. "There is no need to play a sport because I did. I'm proud of who you are, Stevie."

Stevie's desire to try out for the martial arts team was evident by the smile on his face. "Yes, Dad. I want to try one last sport."

There were plenty of boys and girls at the martial arts club. They were every size and shape. Stevie wasn't the smallest one there. The Dojo said, "To be successful, it is not how small you are, but how big is your desire to achieve greatness."

As they passed out jackets of every size, Stevie knew this was the sport for him. He was proud of who he was and was willing to work hard to be the best!